WINTER WONDERLAND
PATTERNS

CREATIVE COLOURING

Michael O'Mara Books Limited

First published in Great Britain in 2015 by
Michael O'Mara Books Limited
9 Lion Yard
Tremadoc Road
London SW4 7NQ

A CIP catalogue record for this book is available from the British Library.

Papers used by Michael O'Mara Books Limited are natural, recyclable products
made from wood grown in sustainable forests. The manufacturing processes
conform to the environmental regulations of the country of origin.

ISBN: 978-1-78243-549-5

4 5 6 7 8 9 10

www.mombooks.com

Cover design by Ana Bjezancevic

Illustrations by Angelea Van Dam, Angelika Scudamore, Carol Spencer,
Emily Hamilton, Faye Buckingham, Fay Martin, Felicity French, Hannah Davies,
James Newman Gray, Jo Taylor, Julie Ingham, Lizzie Preston, Louise Wright,
Rebecca Dinnage and Sally Moret

Cover illustration by Shutterstock

Printed and bound in China

MIX
Paper from
responsible sources
FSC® C010256

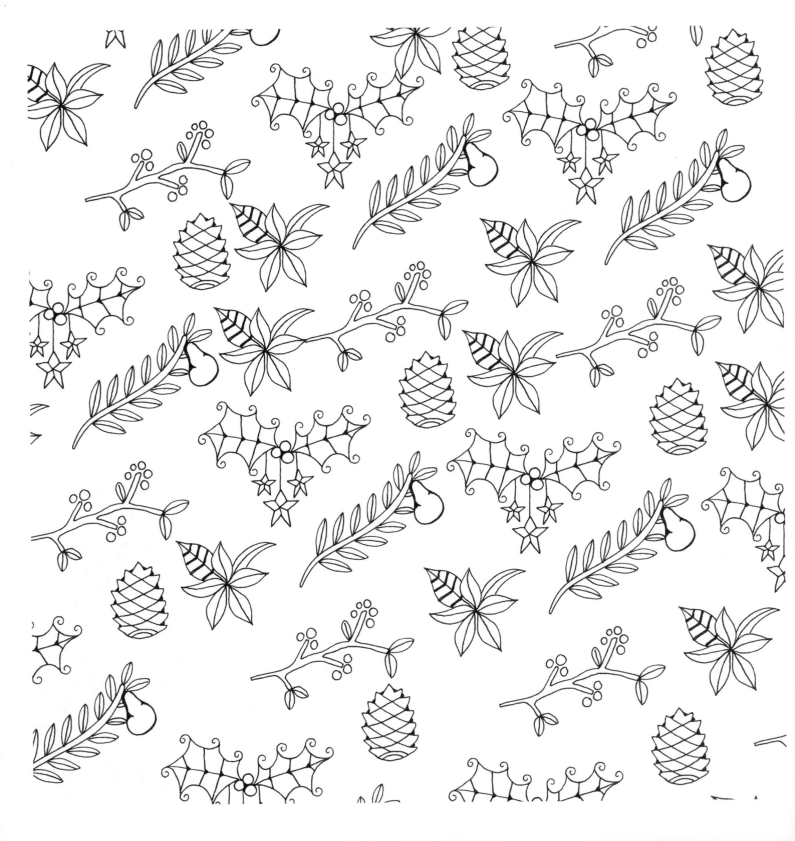

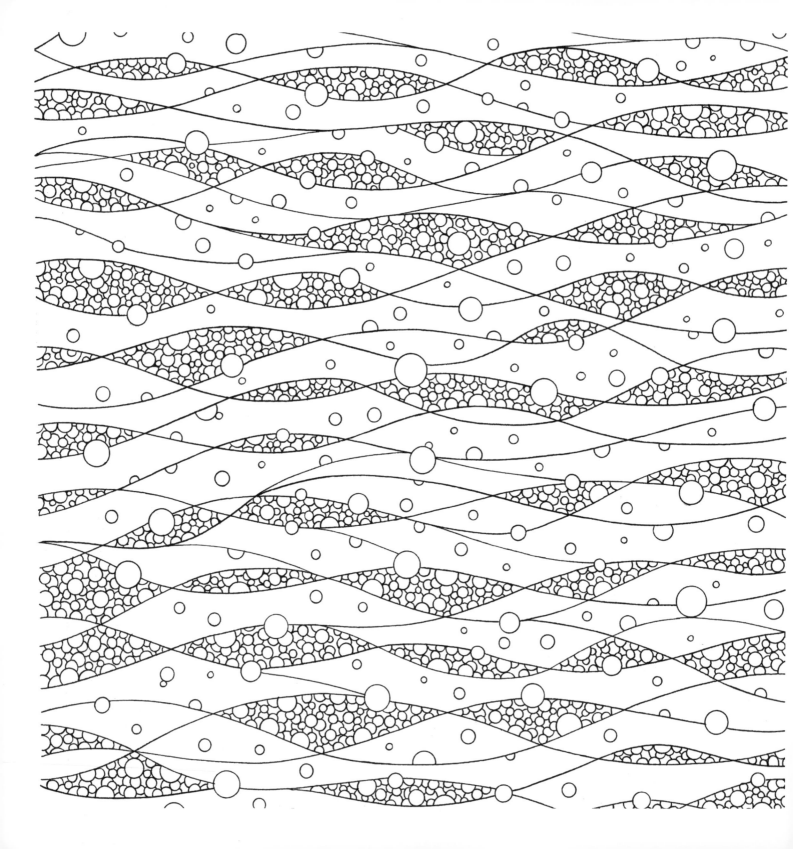